FELIX MENDELSSOHN BARTOLDY

MEERESSTILLE UND GLÜCKLICHE FAHRT

CALM SEA AND PROSPEROUS VOYAGE

Overture for Orchestra
Op. 27

T0081220

Ernst Eulenburg Ltd

London · Mainz · Madrid · New York · Paris · Tokyo · Toronto · Zürich

MEERESSTILLE

Tiefe Stille herrscht im Wasser,
Ohne Regung ruht das Meer,
Und bekümmert sieht der Schiffer
Glatte Fläche rings umher.
Keine Luft von keiner Seite!
Todesstille fürchterlich!
In der ungeheuren Weite
Reget keine Welle sich.

GOETHE.

GLUCKLICHE FAHRT

Die Nebel zerreissen,
Der Himmel ist helle,
Und Æolus löset
Das ängstliche Band.
Es säuseln die Winde,
Es rührt sich der Schiffer,
Geschwinde! Geschwinde!
Es teilt sich die Welle,
Es naht sich die Ferne;
Schon seh' ich das Land!

GOETHE.

CALM AT SEA

Silence deep rules o'er the waters,
Calmly slumbering lies the main,
While the sailor views with trouble
Nought but one vast level plain.

Not a zephyr is in motion!
Silence fearful as the grave!
In the mighty waste of ocean
Sunk to rest is every wave.

THE PROSPEROUS VOYAGE

The mist is fast clearing,
And radiant is heaven,
Whilst Æolus loosens
Our anguish-fraught bond.
The zephyrs are sighing,
Alert is the sailor.
Quick! nimbly be plying!
The billows are riven,
The distance approaches;
I see land beyond!

CALM SEA and PROSPEROUS VOYAGE

(Meeresstille und Glueckliche Fahrt)

OVERTURE

Meeresstille.

Felix Mendelssohn-Bartholdy, Op 27.

1809–1847

4

Glückliche Fahrt

Molto Allegro e vivace

50

E. E. 3751

6

E.E 3751

90

Fl.
Ob.
Cl.
Fg.
Cor.
(D)
Tr.
(D)
Timp.
Vl.
Vla.
Vc.
Cb.

E. E. 3751

11

100

110

140

260

800

E. E. 3751

Picc.

Fl.

Cl.

Fg.

Srp.

Timp

Vl.

Vla

Vc.

Cb.

320

330

40

41

E. E. 3751

380

Picc.

Fl.

Ob.

Cl.

Fg.

Srp.

Cor.
(D)

Tr.
(D)

Timp.

Vl.

Vla.

Vc.

46

400

420

430

50

440

Fl.

Ob.

Cl.

Fg.

Srp.

Cor.
(D)

Tr.
(D)

Timp

Vl.

Vla.

Vc.

Cb.

E.,E.3751

450

51

E. E. 3751

52

E. E. 3751

470

55

480

E. E. 3751

Allegro maestoso. Dasselbe Tempo, die Achtel wie vorher die Viertel.

490